Farmer Charlie through the Seasons

*Dedicated to
Charles Francis Tamashiro
for loving and caring for us
through all the seasons of life.
With love from your family,
the two-legged and the four-legged kind.
Happy 80th Birthday
May 6, 2020*

This is Charlie. He is a farmer. And this is Charlie's tractor. Farmer Charlie uses his tractor all year round.

Early in the spring, when the long winter days begin to warm, Farmer Charlie knows it's time to seed his hay field.

He will grow food for his cows to eat next winter.

Before he can plant grass seed, Farmer Charlie must prepare the soil.

First, he hooks a disc to his tractor.

He pulls the disc across the field to break up the hard ground.

Next, Farmer Charlie attaches a fertilizer hopper to his tractor.

He fills the hopper with fertilizer and drives his tractor up and down the field. The hopper spreads the fertilizer evenly over the freshly turned dirt. This will help the seeds grow into healthy green grass.

But the field is still not ready to plant.

Charlie must harrow the field to break up the big clumps of dirt.

Finally, it is time to plant the seed.

Farmer Charlie hooks a planter to his tractor. He fills each of the bins with Sudan grass seed.

He drives his tractor back and forth across the field.

The planter drills the seed into the ground in straight rows. Small closing wheels cover the seed with dirt.

At last, the field is planted, just in time for the spring rain.

Farmer Charlie waits and watches.

Soon the brown field turns green. The Sudan grass is growing.

Now it is summer. Long days of sunlight help the grass grow tall.

When it grows almost as tall as Charlie, it is time to mow.

Farmer Charlie hooks a swather to his tractor.

The swather cuts the grass,
rolls it through its rollers to condition it,
and then shoots it out in a straight row.

After a day or two, the grass dries into hay. Then, it is ready to be baled. Farmer Charlie attaches a round hay baler to his tractor.

He must drive very slowly while the hay baler scoops up
the rows of hay and winds them into large, round bales.

When it has made a full, round bale, it beeps loudly.
This signals Charlie to stop the tractor.

Slowly, the baler opens wide,
and out plops a big, round bale of hay.

Now it is autumn.

Leaves fall from the trees.

The air feels cool and crisp.

Farmer Charlie uses a tractor fork to stack the bales of hay next to his barn. There they will sit until winter.

Before long, the grass withers,
and snow covers the ground.

Winter is here.

The cows can no longer find green grass to eat,
so Farmer Charlie loads a bale of hay on his tractor fork
and drives it to them.

Using his tractor spool,
he rolls out the hay for his cows.

He will do this every day for as
long as winter lasts.

The cows will eat the hay Charlie stored
until new grass grows in the spring.

Then, when the long winter days begin to warm, Farmer Charlie will know it's time to plant his field again.

CPSIA information can be obtained
at www.ICGtesting.com
Printed in the USA
LVHW072327210420
654201LV00005B/10